Multip

Physics
for You

Keith Johnson

Hutchinson
London Melbourne Auckland Johannesburg

Hutchinson & Co. (Publishers) Ltd

An imprint of the Hutchinson Publishing Group

17-21 Conway Street, London W1P 6JD

Hutchinson Publishing Group (Australia) Pty Ltd
16-22 Church Street, Hawthorn, Melbourne, Victoria 3122

Hutchinson Group (NZ) Ltd
32-34 View Road, PO Box 40-086, Glenfield, Auckland 10

Hutchinson Group (SA) (Pty) Ltd
PO Box 337, Bergvlei 2012, South Africa

First published 1975 as *Multiple Choice Physics for
CSE and O-level* by Bell
This edition published by Hutchinson 1979
Reprinted 1980, 1981, 1982, 1983, 1985

Printed and bound in Great Britain by
Anchor Brendon Ltd, Tiptree, Essex

British Library Cataloguing in Publication Data
Johnson, Keith
　Multiple choice physics for you.
　1. Physics – Examinations, questions, etc.
　I. Title
　530′.076　　　QC32
ISBN 0 09 140521 1

by the same author
Physics for You 1
Physics for You 2
A complete course for CSE Physics

Physics for You O-level edition
A complete course for O-level Physics

Preface

The 300 questions in this book are grouped into 30 sections, each of 10 questions, corresponding to 30 common-core topics that can be expected in all Physics courses leading to C.S.E., 'O' level and similar examinations.

The questions are for use *during* a course rather than at the end of it : each section of 10 questions may be used for classwork or homework, testing or revision, or for practice for examinations, but these 300 questions have been selected for their usefulness in *teaching* Physics as well as testing it. Class discussions of the incorrect as well as the correct responses will help the student to develop and consolidate a clearer understanding of the topic. Ideally, to enhance feedback and to correct false ideas, this discussion should take place soon after the student has completed the section.

Diagrams have been widely used to help the student to understand the question and appreciate the principles involved. In calculations, simple numbers have been used, to keep the arithmetic as straightforward as possible.

I am indebted to my colleague R. D. Palmer for his help in checking the questions and to my wife Ann for her patience.

Manchester   R.K.J.

Contents

Types of Question

1 Multiple Choice
In this type, a question or a statement is followed by five answers, of which only one is correct. You have the choose the one correct answer.
Example 1
Which of the following is a unit of time ?
  A metre
  B kilogramme
  C second
  D newton
  E joule.

Clearly the answer is **C**.

2 Classification Sets
This is a variation on the first type, in which a list of five possible answers is followed by several questions. Each of the five possible answers may be used *once, more than once or not at all.*
Example 2
Here is a list of units :
  A newton
  B joule
  C watt
  D volt
  E ampere.

Which is a unit of force ?

Which is a unit of energy ?

Which is a unit of weight ?

Which is a unit of electrical current ?

The answers are **A, B, A, E** respectively.

3 Multiple Completion

In this type, three responses numbered **1, 2, 3** are suggested. **One or more** of the responses are correct. You have to consider each of the responses in turn and decide whether or not it is a correct answer to the question.

Having decided, you choose

    A if only number **1** is correct
    B if only number **3** is correct
    C if **1** and **2** only are correct
    D if **2** and **3** only are correct
    E if **1, 2** and **3** are correct.

No other combination is used.

Summary				
A	**B**	**C**	**D**	**E**
1 only	3 only	1, 2 only	2, 3 only	1, 2 and 3

The summary is repeated on the back cover.

Example 3

Which of the following units can be used for length ?

    1 Metre.
    2 Millimetre.
    3 Kilogramme.

1 and **2** are correct but **3** is not, so the answer is **C.**

Note : A list of Answers to these questions is available for teachers upon application to the Publishers.

Force

1 A spring balance measures

    1 force
    2 weight
    3 mass.

2 An object is moved from the Earth to the Moon. Which of the following will change ?

    1 The mass of the object.
    2 The weight of the object.
    3 The time taken for the object to fall through 1 metre.

3 A force of 1N

    1 gives a mass of 1kg an acceleration of 1 m/s^2
    2 gives a mass of 2kg an acceleration of 2 m/s^2
    3 gives a mass of 1g an acceleration of 1 cm/s^2.

Questions **4** and **5**.

The diagrams show an object resting on a smooth table with five different systems of force acting on it.

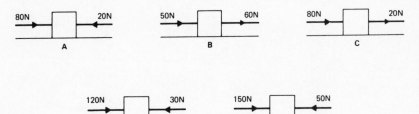

4 In which case will the object have the greatest acceleration ?

5 In which case will the object have the least acceleration ?

6 The diagram shows four spring balances, all pulling on the knot at P as shown. The strings are at 90° to each other.

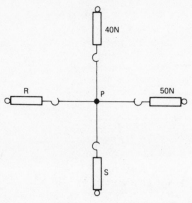

If P is stationary and the readings on two of the balances are as shown, then the readings on R and S are

	R	S
A	50 N	40 N
B	40 N	50 N
C	10 N	90 N
D	90 N	10 N
E	45 N	45 N

Questions **7** and **8**.

The diagrams show a spring with a pointer attached, hanging next to a scale. Three different weights are hung from it in turn, as shown.

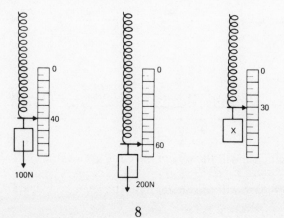

7 If all weight is removed from the spring, which mark on the scale will the pointer indicate ?

     A   zero
     B   10
     C   20
     D   25
     E   30.

8 What is the weight of X ?

     A   −10 N
     B   zero
     C   30 N
     D   50 N
     E   75 N.

9 A mass M, attached to a piece of string OM, is whirled round over a person's head in a *horizontal* circle, centre 0.

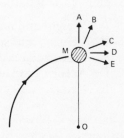

At the position shown, the string suddenly breaks. In which direction does the mass M move after the string breaks ?

10 A boy weighing 500 N falls from a tree. When the boy is in mid-air,

    1 the gravitational force of the Earth on the boy is zero
    2 the gravitational force of the boy on the Earth is 500 N
    3 as the boy falls down to the Earth, the Earth rises up to the boy.

Vectors, Moments

11 Which of these pairs are both scalar quantities ?

    A energy and force
    B speed and mass
    C temperature and velocity
    D volume and weight
    E density and acceleration.

12 Which of these pairs are both vector quantities ?

    A Weight and mass
    B Velocity and speed
    C Force and acceleration
    D Acceleration and speed
    E Velocity and energy.

13 The wind is blowing towards the East. The pilot of an aeroplane wishes to fly due North. In which direction should he aim the aeroplane ?

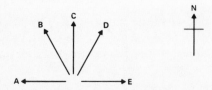

14 Two forces have strengths of 4 N and 6 N. Their resultant force could not possibly be

    A 1 N
    B 2 N
    C 4 N
    D 6 N
    E 10 N.

15 A picture is hung on the wall in three different ways :

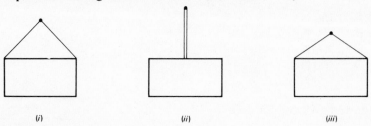

(i) (ii) (iii)

The tension in the string is

  A least in (*i*)
  B greatest in (*i*)
  C greatest in (*ii*)
  D least in (*iii*)
  E greatest in (*iii*).

16 The centre of gravity (centre of mass) of a body is

  1 the point at which the force of gravity can be considered to act
  2 always vertically below or vertically above the point of support when the body is hanging freely
  3 always at the mid-point of the body.

17 The diagram shows a piece of cardboard hanging freely from a nail.

Which point is most likely to indicate the centre of gravity (centre of mass) of the cardboard ?

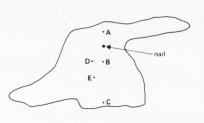

18 A boy weighing 600 N sits on a see-saw at a distance of 1 m from the pivot as shown in the diagram.

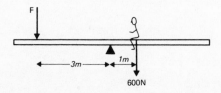

11

What force is needed at F to just balance the see-saw ?

A   150 N
B   200 N
C   300 N
D   400 N
E   1800 N.

Questions **19** and **20**.

A uniform metre rule is balanced as shown :

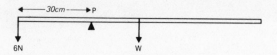

19 The weight W of the metre rule is

A   4 N
B   5 N
C   9 N
D   10 N
E   none of these.

20 The force on the rule at point P is

A   3 N downwards
B   3 N upwards
C   15 N downwards
D   15 N upwards
E   none of these.

Velocity and Acceleration

21 A model train travels 4m in 12s. What is its average speed ?

    A $\frac{1}{3}$ m/s
    B   3 m/s
    C   8 m/s
    D   16 m/s
    E   48 m/s.

22 A racing car accelerates from 10 m/s to 25 m/s in 5 s.
What is the average acceleration ?

    A   3 m/s^2
    B   7 m/s^2
    C   50 m/s^2
    D   75 m/s^2
    E   175 m/s^2.

23 A ball is thrown vertically into the air and when it returns after
an interval of 2 seconds, it is caught. If the acceleration due to
gravity is 10 m/s^2,

    1 the acceleration after it leaves the hand is 10 m/s^2 down-
wards
    2 the ball reaches the top of its flight after 1 second
    3 the acceleration at the top of its flight is 10 m/s^2 downwards.

Questions **24** and **25**.

The diagram shows a velocity-time graph plotted for a car.

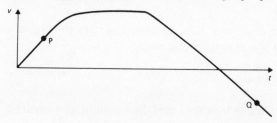

13

24 At point P, the car must be

    A stationary
    B climbing a hill
    C accelerating
    D travelling at constant velocity
    E decelerating.

25 At point Q, the car must be

    A stationary
    B travelling down-hill
    C travelling below ground-level
    D reducing speed
    E travelling in the reverse direction.

Questions **26** and **27**.

The diagrams show several velocity-time graphs.

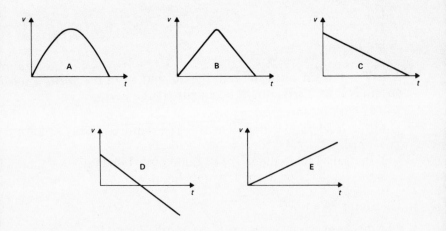

For each question choose the velocity-time graph which most nearly represents the example described.

26 A car braking to a halt.

27 A ball thrown vertically upwards and then caught as it returns.

28 For the ball in question **27**, the corresponding acceleration-time graph is

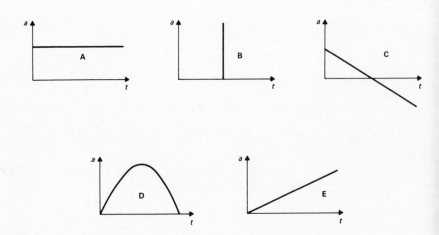

29 The diagram shows a velocity-time graph for a car in a traffic jam.

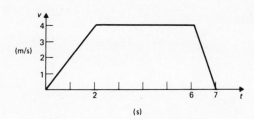

For the car,

1 the initial acceleration is 2 m/s²

2 the maximum velocity is 7 m/s

3 the acceleration between 2 s and 6 s is 1 m/s².

15

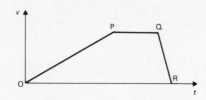

In the velocity-time graph shown,

1 the acceleration from O to P is calculated by the length of the line OP
2 the acceleration from O to P is greater than the deceleration from Q to R
3 the distance travelled during the journey is represented by the area between OPQR and the time axis.

Work, Energy and Power

31 A joule is a unit of

    1 power
    2 heat
    3 kinetic energy.

32 The diagram shows an object of mass 10 kg being pulled for a distance of 3 m by a force of 30 N

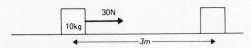

The work done is

    A   9 J
    B   30 J
    C   90 J
    D 300 J
    E 900 J.

33 A box of weight 50 N is pulled 2 m along a horizontal floor by a force of 10 N and then the box is lifted vertically through a height of 1 m.

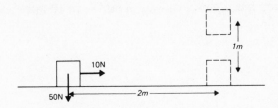

What is the total work done on the box ?

A   35 J
B   55 J
C   70 J
D 110 J
E 180 J

Questions **34** and **35**.

A girl weighing 400 N runs up a flight of stairs of vertical height 5 m in 4 seconds.

34 Her increase in gravitational potential energy is

A 1 600 N
B 1 600 J
C 1 600 W
D 2 000 J
E 2 000 W.

35 Her rate of working against gravity is

A   320 W
B   400 W
C   500 W
D 2 000 W
E 8 000 W.

36 A person when asleep has a power output of 60 W. In 10 minutes his food must provide

A   0·1 J
B   6 J
C   60 J
D   600 J
E 36 000 J.

Questions **37** to **40**.

Here are some possible ways in which energy can change :

A   chemical to heat
B   kinetic to sound
C   kinetic to heat
D   potential to heat
E   potential to kinetic.

Which is the most important change in each of the following examples ?

37 The release of an arrow from a bow.

38 The impact of the arrow in a target.

39 A cyclist riding along a level road at constant velocity.

40 A stone in mid-air, as it falls.

Machines

41 The efficiency of a simple machine is

    1 always less than 100%

    2 equal to $\dfrac{\text{work given out}}{\text{work put in}}$

    3 equal to $\dfrac{\text{velocity ratio}}{\text{mechanical advantage}}$

42 When undoing a tight nut on a car, a mechanic may slide a long steel tube over the spanner so as to make it longer. This

    1 increases the effort needed to undo the nut

    2 reduces the moment (turning effect) of the force he applies

    3 increases the mechanical advantage.

Questions **43** and **44**.

The diagrams show five levers. P marks the pivot, E the effort and L the load.

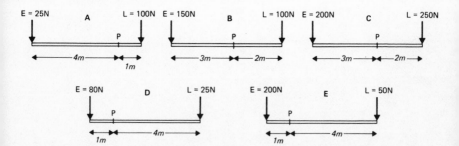

43 Which lever will rotate clockwise ?

44 Which lever will rotate most rapidly anti-clockwise ?

20

Machines

45 A pair of pliers is a simple machine consisting of two levers.

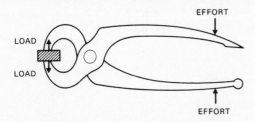

For the pliers shown in the diagram, the mechanical advantage is

    A less than one
    B equal to one
    C greater than one
    D less than 100%
    E equal to 100%.

46 For a pulley system,

    1 the mechanical advantage is always less than the velocity ratio
    2 the velocity ratio equals the number of strings supporting the lower pulley block.
    3 the velocity ratio equals the number of pulleys used.

47

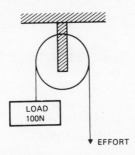

In the absence of friction and neglecting the weight of the string, the effort required to lift the load at constant speed is

    A 50 N
    B 99 N
    C 100 N
    D 101 N
    E 200 N.

Questions **48** and **49**.

The diagrams show some pulley systems. Each system is completely frictionless and the pulleys and ropes are very light compared with the load.

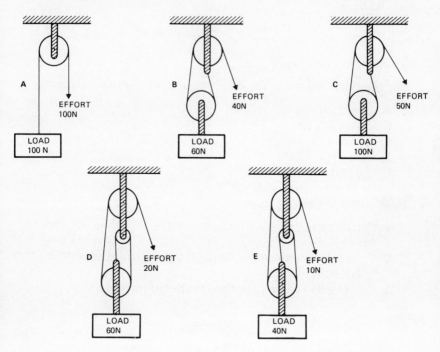

48 In which case would the load be lifted?

49 In which case would the load accelerate downwards most rapidly?

50 In the pulley system shown in the diagram, an effort of 10 N will just lift a load of 25 N.

If the system is completely friction-less, the weight of the lower pulley block is approximately

A 5 N **B** 15 N **C** 30 N **D** 65 N **E** 75 N.

22

Density

Questions **51** and **52**.

The diagrams show (*i*) a spring balance calibrated from 0-100 gf in steps of 10 gf, weighing an object in air (*ii*) a measuring cylinder measuring 0-200 cm³ in steps of 20 cm³ and containing some water (*iii*) the object lowered into the water.

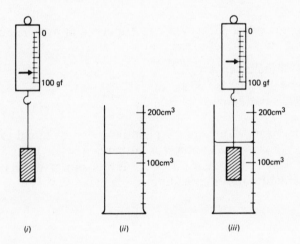

51 Which of these statements is/are correct ?

   1 The weight of the object is 80 gf.
   2 The volume of the water is 120 cm³.
   3 The upthrust on the object when it is in the water is 20 gf.

52 Which of these statements is/are correct ?

   1 The volume of the object is 20 cm³.
   2 The mass of the object is 80 g.
   3 The density of the object is 0·25 g/cm³.

53 A water-tank, full of water, has internal dimensions of 1 m × 2 m × 5 m. The density of water is 1000 kg/m^3. It is correct to say that

   1 the volume of the water is 8 m^3
   2 the formula for calculating the mass of water is mass = volume × density
   3 the mass of the water is 10 000 kg.

54 A bare room measures 5 m × 4 m × 3 m. The density of air is 1·3 kg/m^3. The mass of air in the room is approximately

   A 12 kg
   B 16 kg
   C 46 kg
   D 60 kg
   E 78 kg.

55 A solid rectangular block measures 2 m × 5 m × 4 m and has a mass of 20 000 kg. It is correct to say that

   1 the volume of the block is 40 m^3
   2 the density of the solid is 500 kg/m^3
   3 the block will sink if placed in water.

56 An object is made from a substance which has a density equal to a quarter of that of water. The object is suspended in air from a spring balance which then reads 100 N. If the object is then lowered into a tank of water, the reading on the balance will be

   A zero
   B 25 N
   C 75 N
   D 100 N
   E 400 N.

57 A certain piece of wood floats in liquid X but sinks in liquid Y. This tells us that

   A wood is denser than both X and Y
   B X is denser than Y
   C Y is denser than wood
   D Y is denser than X
   E wood is denser than X.

Density

58 A spring balance is supporting a weight as shown in the diagram. Below it is a beaker of water resting on a compression balance. As the weight is lowered into the water,

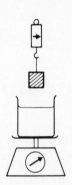

    1 the reading on the spring balance increases

    2 the reading on the compression balance increases

    3 the total of the two readings remains constant.

59 Which of the following statements is/are correct ?

    1 When a swimmer comes out of the water he seems to get heavier.

    2 Ships sink deeper into fresh water than sea-water.

    3 The weight of an object in a vacuum will be found to be more than its weight in air.

60 A hydrometer

    1 is used to measure volume

    2 can be made more sensitive by reducing the width of the stem

    3 will sink further in less dense liquids.

Pressure

61 The pressure exerted on the ground by a man is greatest when

    A he is standing, with both feet flat on the ground
    B he is standing, on both feet, on tip-toe
    C he is standing on one foot, on tip-toe
    D he is sitting on the ground
    E he is lying flat on his back.

62 A man weighing 800 N is wearing snow-shoes. The area of each of his snow-shoes is $\frac{1}{4}$ m². The pressure exerted on the ground by each shoe when he is standing still is

    A   100 N/m²
    B   200 N/m²
    C   400 N/m²
    D 1600 N/m²
    E 3200 N/m².

63 If several cans of different sizes and shapes are all filled to the same depth with the same liquid,

    A the weight of liquid in a can is the same in each case
    B the force on the bottom of a can is the same in each case
    C the least pressure is at the bottom of the largest can
    D the greatest pressure is at the bottom of the largest can
    E the pressure on the bottom is the same in each case.

64 The pressure acting on a submerged submarine depends on

    1 the surface area of the submarine
    2 the depth of the submarine
    3 the density of the water.

65 The pressure at the bottom of a beaker of water depends on

    1 the pressure of the atmosphere above the water surface
    2 the earth's gravitational field strength
    3 the area of the water surface.

66 Referring to the diagram of a U-tube manometer,

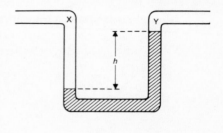

    1 the pressure at X is greater than the pressure at Y

    2 the height *h* depends upon the density of the liquid

    3 the height *h* depends upon the internal diameter of the tube.

67 The fact that the atmosphere exerts a pressure is correctly used to explain

    1 the force holding people to the Earth

    2 the collapse of a metal can when it is evacuated

    3 the support of the mercury column in a mercury barometer.

68 A mercury barometer can be used to measure the

    1 air pressure

    2 height of a mountain

    3 vapour pressure of a liquid.

69 On a day of normal atmospheric pressure, the tube of a mercury barometer is tilted until the top of the tube is a vertical distance of 70 cm above the surface of the mercury in the reservoir. Choose the diagram which best illustrates the appearance of the mercury at the top of the tube.

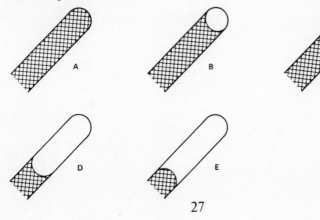

70 The height of the liquid supported by air pressure in a barometer
tube will change if

1 some air is allowed into the space above the liquid in the tube
2 the liquid is changed to one with a different density
3 the tube is changed to one with a different cross-sectional
area.

Kinetic Theory

71 According to the simple Kinetic Theory,

    1 most, but not all, gases consist of molecules
    2 the molecules are in constant motion
    3 the average speed of molecules increases as the temperature increases.

72 Gases are less dense than liquids, because in a gas the molecules are

    A smaller
    B lighter
    C larger
    D moving faster
    E farther apart.

73 The pressure exerted by a gas

    1 is due to the molecules colliding with the walls of the container
    2 will increase if the molecules move faster
    3 will increase if the temperature rises.

74 When air is pumped into a bicycle tyre at constant temperature, the pressure increases because

    A more molecules are hitting the tyre
    B the molecules are larger
    C the molecules are farther apart
    D the molecules are moving faster
    E the molecules have more kinetic energy.

75 Which of the following diagrams is most likely to represent the motion of a molecule in a gas ?

A   B   C   D   E

76 When smoke particles suspended in air are brightly illuminated and viewed through a microscope, they show tiny random movements because

  A the apparatus is vibrating
  B air molecules are bombarding the smoke particles
  C the light waves are shaking the smoke particles
  D sound waves are shaking the smoke particles
  E convection currents are moving the smoke particles.

77 When viewing Brownian motion in a smoke cell,

  1 air molecules can be seen to move
  2 the movement is seen to be regular
  3 if the temperature is lowered, the movement is reduced.

78 The average speed of air molecules in still air at room temperature is approximately

  A zero
  B 2 m/s (walking speed)
  C 30 m/s (fast car)
  D 500 m/s (supersonic aeroplane)
  E 3×10^8 m/s (speed of light).

79 Which of the following can NOT be explained by the movement of molecules ?

  A Diffusion.
  B Conduction.
  C Convection.
  D Radiation.
  E Expansion.

80 When a metal is heated

  1 the kinetic energy of the atoms is increased
  2 the atoms vibrate over a larger distance
  3 the atoms move farther apart from each other.

Expansion

81 Equal volumes of air, iron and water are heated through the same rise in temperature. Arranged in order of increasing expansion, the order is

	least expansion		most expansion
A	air	iron	water
B	iron	water	air
C	water	iron	air
D	air	water	iron
E	iron	air	water

82 When heated,

    A all substances contract
    B all substances expand equally
    C all substances expand but unequally
    D a few substances expand but most contract
    E a few substances contract but most expand.

83 A steel cube is heated from room temperature to 100°C. Which of the following does NOT change?

    A The kinetic energy of the molecules.
    B The surface area of the cube.
    C The mass of the cube.
    D The volume of the cube.
    E The density of the cube.

84 In an experiment, a glass flask is held in both hands, with the result that

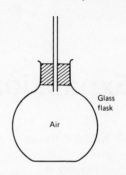

   A nothing happens because air is invisible

   B nothing happens because air and glass expand equally

   C air is squeezed out by the pressure of the hands

   D the glass expands and forces air out

   E the air expands and air is forced out.

85 The diagram shows a bimetal strip connected to an electric bell and a battery.

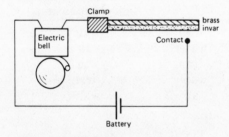

The bimetal strip is made of brass and invar.
Which of the following statements is/are correct?

   1 Brass expands more than invar.

   2 When the temperature rises, the strip bends upwards.

   3 The apparatus could act as a frost alarm.

Questions **86** to **90**.

Which of the following statements

   A useful expansion of a solid

   B useful expansion of a liquid

   C useful expansion of a gas

   D expansion of a solid which is a nuisance

   E expansion of a gas which is a nuisance.

is most appropriate to each of the following examples?

86 An ordinary laboratory thermometer.

Expansion

87 The cracking of a glass tumbler when boiling water is poured in.

88 The loosening of a screw cap from a bottle by placing it under the hot tap.

89 The removal of a dent in a table-tennis ball by placing it in hot water.

90 The danger of throwing an expended aerosol can on a fire.

Thermometers

91 When marking the Lower Fixed Point on a thermometer, the bulb should be placed in ice which is

  1 pure
  2 melting
  3 at a pressure of 100 cm Hg.

92 The Absolute Zero of temperature is

  A −372°C
  B −273°C
  C −273 K
  D   0°C
  E   273 K.

93 The temperatures of the melting point of ice and the boiling point of water are

	melting point	boiling point
A	173 K	273 K
B	273 K	373 K
C	0 K	273 K
D	0 K	100 K
E	0 K	373 K

Thermometers

94 The diagram shows a mercury-in-glass thermometer. When the thermometer is in pure melting ice, the length of the mercury in the stem is 4 cm and when it is in pure steam over boiling water the mercury length is 24 cm.

When placed in a liquid whose temperature is unknown, the mercury length is 19 cm.

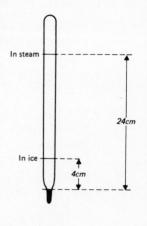

The temperature of the liquid is

   A   63°C
   B   75°C
   C   79°C
   D   95°C
   E   133°C.

95 A mercury-in-glass thermometer will be more sensitive to small changes in temperature if it has

   1 a large bulb
   2 a small diameter bore
   3 a longer stem.

96 A liquid-in-glass thermometer will respond more quickly to changes in temperature if it has

   1 a bulb with thin glass walls
   2 a bulb with a large surface area
   3 a liquid which is a good conductor of heat.

97 A boy was given a thermometer which indicated 1°C for the lower fixed point and 101°C for the upper fixed point. He used the thermometer to measure the temperature of a beaker of cold water. The water was heated and the temperature measured again. He then calculated the rise in temperature of the water. Which of the following is correct?

	1st reading	2nd reading	calculated rise in temperature
A	too high	too high	too high
B	too high	too high	correct
C	too high	too high	too low
D	too low	too low	correct
E	too low	too low	too high

98 Which of the following can be safely washed in boiling water ?

    1 mercury-in-glass thermometer
    2 alcohol-in-glass thermometer
    3 clinical thermometer.

99 When considering mercury and alcohol as thermometric liquids,

    1 mercury can be used at lower temperatures than alcohol
    2 mercury expands more than alcohol
    3 mercury is a better conductor than alcohol.

100 A clinical thermometer contains a constriction in the bore of the tube in order to

    A give a steady reading of $36 \cdot 9°C$.
    B keep the mercury at its maximum reading
    C keep the mercury at its minimum reading
    D indicate where the temperature should be read
    E give a quicker reading.

Heat Energy

101 Equal amounts of hot and cold water are run into a bath. The hot water is at 50°C and the cold water is at 10°C. The temperature of the mixture will be approximately

    A 10°C
    B 20°C
    C 30°C
    D 40°C
    E 50°C.

102 2 kg of water at 10°C is mixed with 4 kg of water at 70°C. If no heat is lost, the temperature of the mixture will be

    A 20°C
    B 30°C
    C 40°C
    D 50°C
    E 60°C.

103 Mark pours some water into a beaker and so does Anne. They both begin to heat their beakers at the same time but Mark's water boils first. Which of the following statements could explain this ?

    1 Mark's water was initially warmer than Anne's.
    2 Anne has more water to heat.
    3 Anne's beaker is heavier than Mark's.

104 Two cubes of copper, X and Y, are each heated by an electric heater. The graphs of temperature against time are as shown.

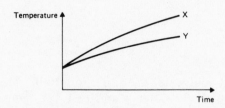

From this information, a scientist would conclude that

A heater X is more powerful than heater Y
B Y is in a draught
C X is wrapped in cotton wool
D Y is heavier than X
E any of the previous statements could be correct but none is certain.

105 2 000 J of energy are need to heat 1 kg of paraffin through 1°C. How much heat is needed to raise 2 kg of paraffin through 10°C?

A   4 000 J
B   10 000 J
C   20 000 J
D   24 000 J
E   40 000 J.

106 800 J of energy are needed to heat 1 kg of aluminium through 1°C. If 8 000 J are given to 2 kg of aluminium, the rise in temperature will be

A   2·5°C
B   5°C
C   10°C
D   15°C
E   20°C.

Questions **107** and **108**.

400 J of energy are needed to heat 1 kg of copper through 1°C. When 1 g of wood is completely burned the amount of heat released is 20 000 J.

107 If 20 g of wood is completely burned, the amount of heat released is

    A   1 000 J
    B   4 000 J
    C   40 000 J
    D   400 000 J
    E 4 000 000 J.

108 If all the energy from the wood is given to 10 kg of copper, the rise in temperature is   *use 20 g wood.*

    A   16°C
    B   100°C
    C   160°C
    D 1 000°C
    E 1 600°C.

109 How many joules of heat energy are supplied by a 2 kW heater running for 10 seconds ?

    A   20 J
    B   200 J
    C   2 000 J
    D   20 000 J
    E 200 000 J.

110 An electric refrigerator at room temperature is switched on with its door open in a completely insulated room.
Over a period of time, the temperature of the room is found **to**

    A   rise steadily
    B   rise then fall
    C   fall steadily
    D   fall then rise
    E   remain constant.

Change of State

Questions **111** to **113**.

A substance is heated at a constant rate and a graph of temperature against time is drawn :

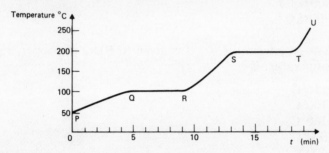

111 Which parts of the graph correspond to the solid, liquid and gas states ?

	solid	liquid	gas
A	PQ	QR	RS
B	PQ	RS	TU
C	QR	RS	ST
D	TU	RS	PQ
E	ST	RS	QR

112 During which parts of the graph is the substance taking in latent heat ?

  A PQ only
  B RS only
  C TU only
  D QR and ST
  E PQ, RS and TU.

113 What is the Freezing Point of the substance ?

    A   50°C
    B 100°C
    C 150°C
    D 200°C
    E 250°C.

114 When a liquid boils, the energy which the molecules need to escape from the liquid comes from

    1 atmospheric pressure
    2 within the molecule itself
    3 the heat supplied to the liquid.

115 1kg of ice at 0°C needs 330 000 J of heat just to melt it. Similarly, the specific latent heat of steam is 2 300 000 J/kg. The heat needed to boil 2 kg of water at 100°C to steam is

    A   165 000 J
    B   660 000 J
    C 1 150 000 J
    D 2 630 000 J
    E 4 600 000 J.

116 A pool of liquid on the bench is evaporating. As it evaporates,

    1 the molecules which leave the liquid are those which have higher-than-average speeds
    2 the average speed of the remaining molecules is lowered
    3 the temperature of the liquid falls.

117 The Boiling Point of pure water can be raised to 101°C by

    1 heating it more rapidly
    2 increasing the external pressure
    3 adding salt.

118 The Freezing Point of pure water can be lowered to −1°C by

    1 cooling it more rapidly
    2 increasing the external pressure
    3 adding salt.

119 Metal water pipes sometimes burst in cold weather because

    A the metal becomes more brittle
    B the metal contracts more than the water
    C the inside and the outside of the pipe contract by different amounts
    D when the ice melts, it expands
    E when the water freezes, it expands.

120 Which one of the following graphs of volume (V) against temperature (*t*) most nearly shows the change in volume of water as it is heated from −10°C to +10°C ?

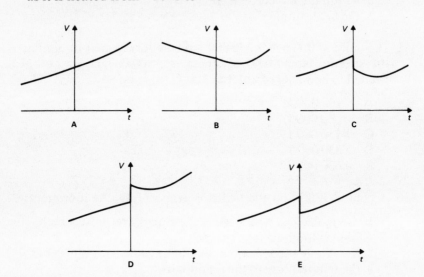

Transfer of Heat

121 In the experiment shown in the diagram, the water at the top of the tube boils before the ice melts.

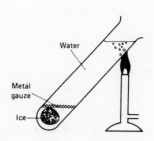

This demonstrates that

A ice is a poor conductor of heat
B water is a poor conductor of heat
C ice is heavier than water
D the metal gauze conducts the heat away from the ice
E there are no convection currents.

Questions **122** to **125**.

Heat can be transferred by :

A Conduction only.
B Convection only.
C Radiation only.
D Conduction and Radiation.
E Conduction, Convection and Radiation.

For each of the next four questions, choose from **A—E** the most appropriate response to describe the transfer of heat.

122 Through the base of a saucepan.

123 Through a glass window.

124 From the Sun to the Earth.

125 From a gas fire to the room.

126 In a heat experiment, which of the following will NOT reduce the heat lost from a can of hot water ?

    A Lagging the outside of the can.
    B Covering the opening with a lid.
    C Polishing the outside of the can.
    D Placing it in a draught-free box.
    E Stirring the water.

127 Mark pours some boiling water into a painted metal can and so does Anne at the same time. Both cans are left to cool on the same table, but Mark's can cools faster than Anne's.
Which of the following statements could explain this ?

    1 The outside of Mark's can is rougher than Anne's.
    2 The outside of Mark's can is blacker than Anne's.
    3 Mark's can has a smaller surface area than Anne's.

Question **128** and **129**.

In an experiment to investigate the absorption of heat rays, two metal cans, each containing water, were placed equal distances from a red-hot heater. Thermometers were used to record the temperatures.

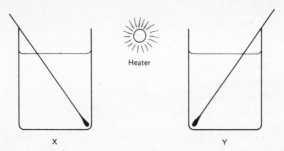

The outside of X was polished brightly and the outside of Y was painted dull black.

128 For valid conclusions to be made in this experiment,

    1 the cans should be identical in size and material
    2 the initial temperature of each can of water should be the same
    3 the cans need not contain equal masses of water.

129 In this experiment,

   1 the energy arriving at can Y is greater than that arriving at can X

   2 the energy absorbed by can Y is greater than that absorbed by can X

   3 the rise in temperature of can Y is greater than that of can X.

130 With reference to a vacuum flask, which of the following statements is NOT correct ?

   A The silvering reduces heat transfer by radiation.
   B The vacuum reduces heat transfer by conduction.
   C The vacuum reduces heat transfer by convection.
   D The vacuum reduces heat transfer by radiation.
   E Using glass for the double walls reduces heat transfer by conduction.

Waves

Questions **131** and **132**.

The diagram shows the side view of a travelling transverse wave.

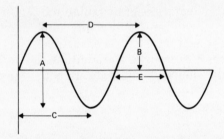

131 Which distance is the amplitude of the wave ?

132 Which distance is the wavelength ?

133 Reflection can occur with

    1 light waves
    2 sound waves
    3 water waves.

Questions **134** and **135**.

A straight wooden bar oscillates up and down in a ripple tank at 2 Hz and produces plane waves as shown in the diagram. Points X and Y are 60 cm apart.

134 The wavelength is

    A 10 cm
    B 30 cm
    C 35 cm
    D 60 cm
    E 70 cm.

Waves

135 The velocity of the wave is

    A   5 cm/s
    B   10 cm/s
    C   20 cm/s
    D   30 cm/s
    E 120 cm/s.

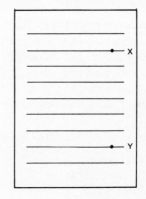

136 The diagram shows the top view of a ripple tank, with a boundary PQ between deep and shallow water. Straight waves are travelling towards the boundary at an angle as shown.

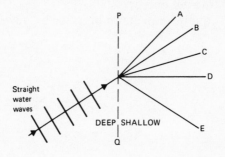

Choose the letter which indicates most nearly the new direction of travel of the waves.

137 When waves in a ripple tank pass from deep water to shallow water,

    1 their frequency is less in the shallower water
    2 their wavelength is less in the shallower water
    3 their velocity is less in the shallower water.

138 With reference to a ripple tank, which of the following statements is/are correct ?

> **1** When a straight wavefront in water hits a straight barrier, it is reflected as a straight wave.
>
> **2** When a circular wavefront in water hits a straight barrier, it is reflected in a circular wave.
>
> **3** When a straight wavefront in water hits a concave circular barrier, it is reflected to one point.

139 An example of a transverse wave is

> **1** a water wave
> **2** ultra-violet light
> **3** a sound wave.

140 Which of the following statements can be correctly applied to both transverse and longitudinal waves ?

> **1** They all travel at the same speed.
> **2** They all transfer energy.
> **3** Velocity equals frequency multiplied by wavelength.

Sound

141 Sound waves

    1 always require a material medium through which to travel
    2 always originate from a vibrating source
    3 travel in a direction at right angles to the direction of displacement of the molecules.

142 The graphs below are of two sound waves in air drawn to the same scale.

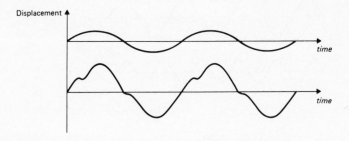

These notes *differ* in

    1 frequency
    2 amplitude
    3 quality (tone).

143 A source of sound emits a note of frequency 600 Hz (cycles per second). If the velocity of sound is 300 m/s, the wavelength is

    A   0·5 m
    B   2 m
    C   300 m
    D   900 m
    E 180 000 m.

144 A source of sound of frequency 150 Hz emits waves of wavelength 2 m. How far will the waves travel in 5 seconds ?

    A   15 m
    B   75 m
    C   300 m
    D   750 m
    E 1500 m.

145 The velocity of sound in air

    1 depends on the frequency of the note
    2 is faster than the velocity of sound in water
    3 increases as the temperature increases.

146 The graphs below are of two sound waves in air drawn to the same scale.

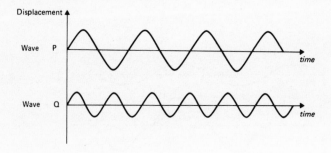

Which is the correct statement ?

    A Wave P is louder than Q and at a lower frequency
    B Wave P is louder than Q and at a higher frequency
    C Wave Q is louder than P and at a lower frequency
    D Wave Q is louder than P and at a higher frequency
    E Wave P is louder than Q and they have the same frequency.

147 To measure the velocity of sound, a man could shout and then listen to his echo from a cliff. To calculate the velocity of sound he would need to know

    1 the time interval between shouting and hearing the echo
    2 his distance from the cliff
    3 the wavelength of the sound waves.

148 An echo-sounder on a ship sends sound waves vertically downwards to the sea-bed. The echo is received after an interval of 4 seconds. If the velocity of sound in sea-water is 1 500 m/s, the depth of the sea beneath the ship is

    A   375 m
    B   750 m
    C   3 000 m
    D   6 000 m
    E 12 000 m.

149 The frequency of the note emitted by a guitar string can be increased by

    1 increasing the tension
    2 decreasing the length
    3 using a heavier string.

150 The graph below shows the pressure variation of a sound wave as displayed on a cathode ray oscilloscope connected to a microphone.

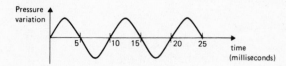

The frequency of the wave is

    A 50 Hz   **B** 100 Hz   **C** 200 Hz   **D** 5 000 Hz   **E** 10 000 Hz.

Light Rays, Mirrors

151 The image of a house formed by a pin-hole camera is

    1 inverted
    2 real
    3 magnified.

152 If the pin-hole of a pin-hole camera is made larger, the image is

    A brighter and sharper
    B brighter and blurred
    C fainter and sharper
    D fainter and blurred
    E unchanged.

153 An eclipse of the Moon occurs when

    1 there is a full Moon
    2 the Earth is between the Sun and the Moon
    3 the Moon moves into the shadow of the Earth.

154 The diagram shows a ray of light reflected from a plane mirror.

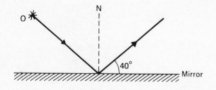

The angle of incidence is

    A 20°
    B 40°
    C 50°
    D 60°
    E 90°.

155 The image in a plane mirror is

    1 real
    2 magnified
    3 laterally inverted.

156 The image in a plane mirror is

    1 on the normal from the object
    2 on the other side of the mirror
    3 as far from the mirror as the object is.

157 A plane mirror is often built in to the scale of an ammeter. This is to

    A illuminate the scale
    B make the pointer easier to see
    C make sure the pointer is straight
    D make sure the scale is viewed perpendicularly
    E magnify the movement of the pointer.

158 Which one of the following diagrams (of an F-shaped object and a plane mirror) shows the image drawn correctly ?

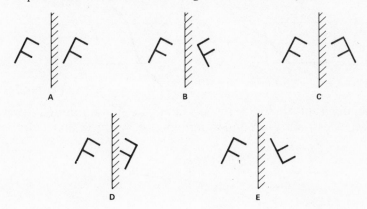

159 Convex mirrors

    1 always give a diminished erect image of an object
    2 have a wide field of view (as in a driving mirror)
    3 can produce a parallel beam of light from a small source.

160 Concave mirrors

    1 can give a magnified erect image of a near object (as in a shaving or make-up mirror)
    2 can concentrate the sun's rays to produce intense heat at a spot
    3 always produce real images.

Refraction

161 The diagrams show a light ray entering a rectangular glass block from air. Choose the one correct diagram.

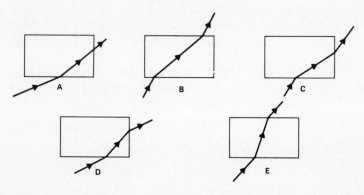

162 The diagram shows a ray of light travelling through three substances—air, glass and water, not necessarily in that order.

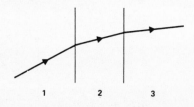

If light travels most quickly in air and most slowly in glass, then the substances 1, 2 and 3 could be

	1	2	3
A	glass	water	air
B	air	glass	water
C	water	glass	air
D	air	water	glass
E	glass	air	water

54

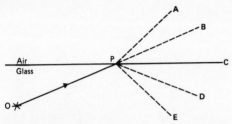

To which point does the ray OP in the diagram travel ?

Questions **164** to **166**.

The following diagrams show a ray of light passing through a glass prism with angles of 45°, 45°, 90°.

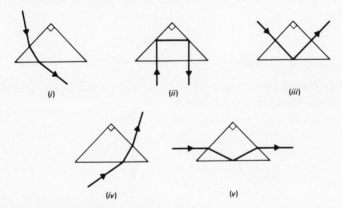

164 The correct diagrams are

    A (*i*) and (*iv*) only
    B (*ii*) and (*iii*) only
    C (*i*), (*iv*) and (*v*) only
    D (*i*), (*ii*), (*iii*) and (*iv*) only
    E all of them.

165 Which diagram shows a prism used as in a periscope ?

    A (*i*)
    B (*ii*)
    C (*iii*)
    D (*iv*)
    E (*v*).

166 Which diagram shows a prism used as in a bicycle reflector ?

    A (*i*)
    B (*ii*)
    C (*iii*)
    D (*iv*)
    E (*v*).

167 As a ray of red light passes from air into glass at an oblique angle,

    1 its velocity decreases
    2 its wavelength decreases
    3 it is refracted through a smaller angle than blue light would be.

Questions **168** and **169**.

The diagram shows a boy at the side of a swimming pool looking down at an object in the water.

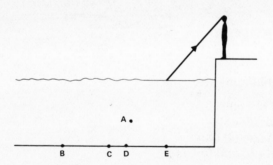

168 If he is looking in the direction shown, which object can he see ?

169 Where does this object appear to be to the boy ?

170 For which piece of glass is the ray diagram correct ?

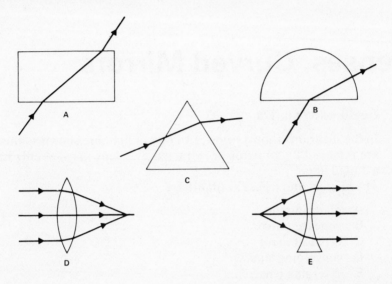

Lenses, Curved Mirrors

Questions **171** to **174**.

In the diagrams shown below, two rays of light are shown as they are reflected by a mirror or refracted by a lens marked only by a dotted line.

The mirrors and lenses available are

A plane mirror
B concave mirror
C convex mirror
D converging lens
E diverging lens.

For each of the questions **171** to **174** choose the correct mirror or lens.

171

172

173

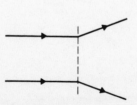

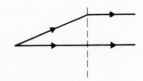

Questions 175 and **176**.

The diagram shows 5 rays from the top of an object drawn through a converging lens. Three rays are the correctly drawn constructions you would use to find the top of the image.

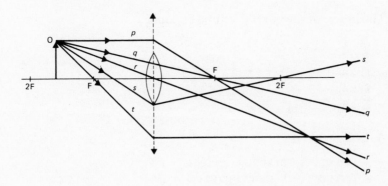

175 Which two rays are *not* drawn correctly ?

    A p and q
    B p and t
    C q and s
    D q and t
    E s and t

176 The image formed by the correct rays is

    1 virtual
    2 erect
    3 magnified.

177 The diagram below shows an object OP placed near a converging lens.

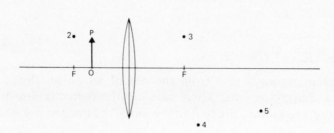

The image of the point P will be at point

A 1
B 2
C 3
D 4
E 5.

178 A diverging lens

1 can only form virtual images
2 can only form erect images
3 can only form diminished images.

179 In comparing the human eye and a camera, it is found that

1 they both contain diverging lenses
2 the eye can focus on nearer objects by reducing the focal length of its lens
3 the camera can focus on nearer objects by moving the lens farther from the film.

180 A person has an eye defect. When he looks at a distant object, the image is formed in front of the retina. This means that

1 he has short sight (myopia)
2 his eye lens is too powerful or his eye-ball is too long
3 his sight could be corrected by using a diverging spectacle lens.

Spectra, Colour

181 The diagrams show white light passing into a 60°—60°—60° prism.

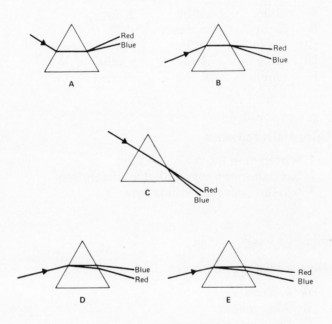

Which one of these diagrams is correct ?

182 What is the correct order of increasing wavelength for these colours of the visible spectrum ?

    A red   yellow   green   blue
    B red   green   yellow   blue
    C green   yellow   blue   red
    D blue   green   yellow   red
    E blue   yellow   green   red.

183 The diagram shows part of a chart of the full electromagnetic spectrum in order of wavelength.

Gamma rays	P	ultra-violet	Q	infra-red	R

The sections marked P, Q and R could be

	P	Q	R
A	radio	visible	X-ray
B	X-ray	visible	radio
C	X-ray	radio	visible
D	radio	X-ray	visible
E	visible	X-ray	radio

184 Ultra-violet radiation

    1 is present in the sun's radiation
    2 has a shorter wavelength than visible light
    3 travels faster than visible light.

Questions **185** and **186**.

Here is a list of apparatus :

    A Camera
    B Microphone
    C Gold leaf electroscope
    D Geiger counter
    E Radio receiver.

185 Which instrument is used to detect radiation which has a wavelength between that of infra-red and ultra-violet radiation ?

186 Which instrument is usually preferred to detect radiation which has a wavelength shorter than X-rays ?

187 Which of the following waves does NOT travel at the same speed as radio waves ?

    A X-rays
    B infra-red
    C visible
    D sound
    E gamma rays.

188 A pure red lipstick, when viewed in the pure yellow light from a sodium street lamp, looks

    A red
    B orange
    C yellow
    D white
    E black.

189 The diagram shows white light shining on to a red book. The book is then viewed through a magenta filter.

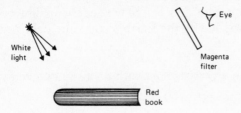

The book appears to be

    A red
    B blue
    C magenta
    D yellow
    E black.

190 A red dress with yellow spots is viewed in green light.
It will appear

    A completely green
    B completely yellow
    C black with green spots
    D yellow with green spots
    E green with black spots.

Magnetism

191 Which of the following tests is the most satisfactory for deciding whether a metal bar is magnetised ?

    A Chemical analysis to see if the metal is iron.
    B Iron filings stick to one end of the bar.
    C A compass needle is repelled by the bar.
    D A compass needle is attracted by the bar.
    E When freely suspended, the bar points toward the nearest magnet.

192 A piece of steel may be magnetised by

    1 stroking it with a magnet
    2 placing it inside a coil of wire carrying direct current
    3 aligning it with the Earth's magnetic field and hammering it.

193 An iron bar PQ is stroked with a strong magnet as shown in the diagram.

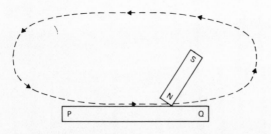

The resulting polarity

    A is a south pole at P and a north pole at Q
    B is a north pole at P and a south pole at Q
    C depends on where the stroking begins
    D depends on the speed of the first stroke
    E can only be determined using a compass.

194 Two rods PQ and XY were brought near to the north pole of a magnet. With the first rod, both ends P and Q were attracted by the magnet. With the second rod, end X was attracted and end Y was repelled.

These tests suggest that

  1 PQ was a magnet
  2 PQ was made from material which can be magnetised
  3 Y was a north pole.

195 The magnetism of a steel bar can be reduced by

  1 heating it
  2 hammering it
  3 gradually removing it from inside a coil of wire carrying an alternating current.

196 Lines of force

  1 go from a N-pole to a S-pole
  2 never cross each other
  3 are closer together where the magnetic field is stronger.

Questions **197** to **199**.

Here are some diagrams of possible magnetic fields :

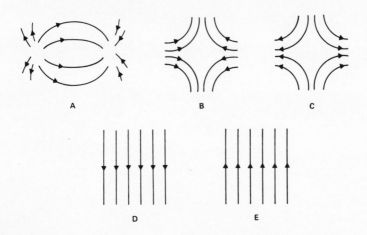

197 Which represents the field due to a single bar magnet ?

198 Which represents the field due to two magnets placed like this :

199 Which represents the Earth's magnetic field at your present position, if magnetic north is in the direction shown here ?

200 The molecular theory of magnetism can explain each of the following EXCEPT,

    A a N-pole attracts a S-pole
    B stroking with a magnet will magnetise an iron bar
    C when a magnet is broken in two, each part is a magnet
    D heating destroys magnetisation
    E hammering reduces magnetisation.

Electrostatics

201 A negatively charged rod will

  1 repel a negative charge
  2 attract a positive charge
  3 always point north—south when freely suspended.

Questions **202** and **203**.

A plastic rod is rubbed on a dry cloth and the rod becomes positively charged.

202 The rod has

  A gained electrons
  B lost electrons
  C gained protons
  D lost protons
  E changed some electrons into protons.

203 The cloth has

  A a positive charge equal to that on the rod
  B a negative charge equal to that on the rod
  C a positive charge less than that on the rod
  D a negative charge greater than that on the rod
  E no charge.

204 P and Q are metal balls hanging from nylon threads. When a negatively charged rod is placed between them as shown, P is repelled and Q is attracted by the rod.

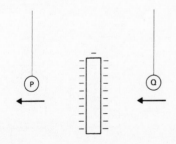

Which of the following statements can be deduced?

  1 P must be negative.
  2 Q could be positive.
  3 Q could be uncharged.

Questions 205 and 206.

In an experiment 4 plastic rods P, Q, R, S are used. Each rod may be charged or uncharged. In tests, it is found that P repels Q but R exerts no force on S.

 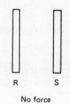

205 These tests show that

  A P and Q are both positive
  B P and Q are both negative
  C P and Q have opposite charges
  D R and S have opposite charges
  E R and S are uncharged.

206 In further tests it would be found that

  A P would attract R
  B P would repel S
  C P would repel R
  D Q would repel R
  E Q would repel S.

207 Which of these diagrams represents the effect of bringing a positively-charged rod near to (but not touching) a gold-leaf electroscope.

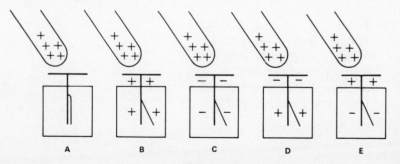

208 A gold-leaf electroscope is negatively charged, with the leaf at an angle of about 45°.

When a negatively charged rod is slowly brought near the plate of the electroscope, the leaf

    A rises
    B falls
    C rises then falls
    D falls to zero then rises
    E does not move.

209 A gold-leaf electroscope is negatively charged with the leaf at an angle of about 45°. A metal ball on an insulating handle is slowly brought near to (but not touching) the plate of the electroscope and the leaf falls.

This suggests that the metal ball is

    A uncharged
    B uncharged or positively charged
    C uncharged or negatively charged
    D positively charged
    E negatively charged.

210 A pear-shaped conductor stands on an insulated base as shown.

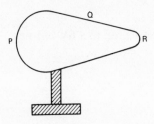

If the conductor is given some charge at P,

    1 all the charge stays on the surface of the conductor
    2 the charge density (amount of charge per unit area) is lowest at Q
    3 the charge density is highest at P.

Circuits

211 The diagram shows a circuit for testing two rods, one of plastic and one of metal.

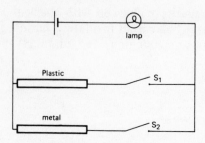

The lamp will light if

1 only switch S_1 is closed
2 only switch S_2 is closed
3 both switches are closed.

212 The diagram shows two 6V lamps connected to a 6V battery.

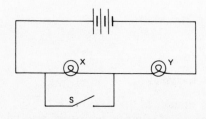

When the switch S is closed,

A Y glows brighter and X goes out
B X glows brighter and Y goes out
C both lamps go out
D both lamps glow less brightly
E both lamps glow more brightly.

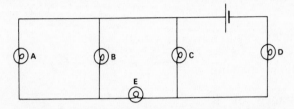

In this circuit, one of the lamps has fused and caused all the lamps to go out.
Which lamp has fused ?

214 The diagram shows a junction in a circuit with four ammeters. The readings of three of the ammeters are shown.

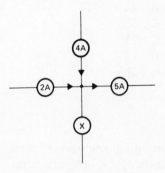

The reading on X is

A zero
B 1A
C 3A
D 7A
E 11A.

215

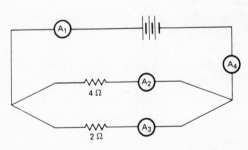

The diagram shows four identical ammeters connected in a circuit.

1 The reading on A_1 is the same as the reading on A_4.
2 The reading on A_2 is less than the reading on A_1.
3 The reading on A_2 is less than the reading on A_3.

71

216 In this circuit, when the resistance of the rheostat is decreased,

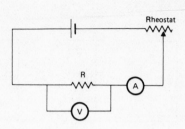

    1 the ammeter reading increases

    2 the voltmeter reading increases

    3 the resistance of R decreases.

217 If in this circuit V_1 reads 6V, the reading on V_2 is

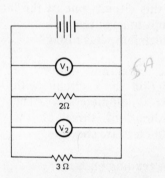

    A 4V
    B 6V
    C 9V
    D 12V
    E 18V.

218 The diagram shows three identical voltmeters connected in a circuit.

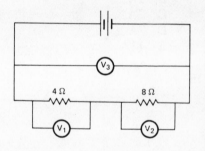

    1 The reading on V_3 is greater than the reading on V_2.

    2 The reading on V_1 is half the reading on V_2.

    3 The reading on V_1 is one third of the reading on V_3.

219

An ammeter

    1 should have a low resistance

    2 may be made from a galvanometer by adding a low resistance in parallel

    3 is always placed in parallel with other components in a circuit.

220 A voltmeter

1 should have a high resistance
2 may be made from a galvanometer by adding a high resistance in parallel
3 is always placed in series with other components in a circuit.

Ohm's Law

221 In this circuit, the reading on the ammeter is 2 A.

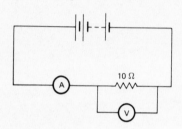

The reading on the voltmeter is

A   2 V
B   5 V
C   8 V
D   12 V
E   20 V.

Questions **222** and **223**.

In this circuit, the voltmeter reading is 12 V.

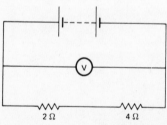

222 The combined resistance of the 2 Ω and 4 Ω resistors in series is

A   2 Ω
B   3 Ω
C   4 Ω
D   6 Ω
E   8 Ω.

223 The current flowing through these resistors is

    A   2 A

    B   3 A

    C   4 A

    D   6 A

    E 12 A.

224 The resistance of a copper wire is reduced if the wire is made

    1 shorter

    2 thicker

    3 hotter.

225 Which of the following statements is NOT correct ?

    A 1 MΩ (1 Megohm) = 1 000 000 Ω

    B 1 kV (1 kilovolt) = 1 000 V

    C 1 mA (1 milliamp) = $\dfrac{1}{1\,000}$ A

    D 1 μA (1 microamp) = $\dfrac{1}{100\,000}$ A

    E 1 nA (1 nanoamp) = $\dfrac{1}{1\,000\,000\,000}$ A.

Questions **226** and **227**.

The diagram shows two cells connected to a 2Ω resistor.

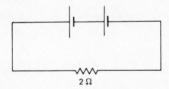

226 What current flows when each cell has an e.m.f. of 2V and no internal resistance ?

    A $\frac{1}{2}$A   **B** 1 A   **C** 2 A   **D** 4 A   **E** 6 A.

227 What current flows when each cell has an e.m.f. of 2 V and each has an internal resistance of 1 Ω ?

    A $\frac{1}{2}$A   **B** 1 A   **C** 2 A   **D** 4 A   **E** 6 A.

Questions **228** to **230**.

Look at this circuit diagram.

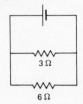

Now compare it with these four diagrams

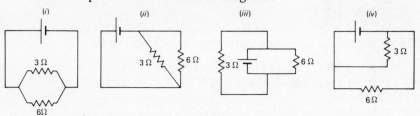

228 The original circuit diagram is the same electrical circuit as

    A   (*i*) only
    B   (*i*) and (*ii*) only
    C   (*ii*) and (*iii*) only
    D   (*i*), (*ii*) and (*iv*) only
    E   (*i*), (*ii*), (*iii*) and (*iv*).

229 What is the combined resistance of the resistors in the original circuit ?

    A $\frac{1}{2}$ ohm
    B   2 ohm
    C $4\frac{1}{2}$ ohm
    D   9 ohm
    E   18 ohm.

230 If the circuit is powered by a 2 V accumulator, what current is taken ?

    A $\frac{1}{4}$ A
    B   1 A
    C $2\frac{1}{4}$ A
    D   4 A
    E   9 A.

Electrical Heating

231 An electrical heater produces 10 000 J of heat in 100 seconds.
The power rating of the heater is

    A   0·1 kW
    B   1 kW
    C   10 kW
    D 100 kW
    E 1000 kW.

232 In the circuit shown, the
ammeter reading is 2 A.

The power dissipated in the
10Ω resistor is

    A 2·5 W
    B   5 W
    C 20 W
    D 40 W
    E 200 W.

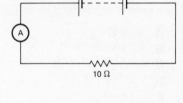

Questions **233** and **234**.

A car headlamp is labelled 12 V, 48 W.

233 At its working temperature, the current through the filament is

    A $\frac{1}{4}$ A
    B   3 A
    C   4 A
    D 12 A
    E 36 A.

234 At its working temperature, the resistance of the filament is

> **A** $\frac{1}{4}$ Ω
> **B** 3 Ω
> **C** 4 Ω
> **D** 12 Ω
> **E** 36 Ω.

Questions **235** and **236**.

The diagram shows a battery connected to an electrical heater in a can of water.

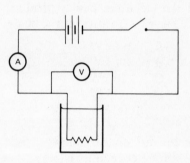

The current is switched on for exactly 1 minute and the ammeter reads 3 A while the voltmeter reads 6 V.

235 The power dissipated by the heater is

> **A** 0·5 W
> **B** 2 W
> **C** 3 W
> **D** 9 W
> **E** 18 W.

236 The heat given to the water is

> **A** 18 J
> **B** 30 J
> **C** 120 J
> **D** 540 J
> **E** 1080 J.

237 If the cost of 1 unit (kWh) of electricity is 2p, what is the cost of running a 3 kW electric fire for 4 hours ?

> **A** 6p
> **B** 8p
> **C** 12p
> **D** 24p
> **E** 48p.

238 If an electric heater has a resistance of 25 Ω and is used on a 250 volt supply for 2 hours,

    1 the current taken is 10 A
    2 the power rating of the heater is 2·5 kW
    3 the energy consumed is 5 kWh.

239 The diagram shows a modern fused 13 A mains plug.

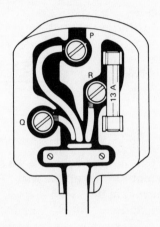

Which of the following statements is NOT correct ?

    A The plug should always be fitted with a 13 A fuse.
    B P is the earth pin.
    C The green/yellow wire should be connected to P.
    D The blue wire should be connected to Q.
    E The brown wire should be connected to R.

240 A 800 W hair dryer is used on a 250-volt supply.
What value of fuse should be fitted in the plug ?

    A   2 A
    B   3 A
    C   5 A
    D 13 A
    E 15 A.

Electromagnetism

241 The diagram shows a horizontal board with a vertical wire running through it. Four small compasses are placed on the board.

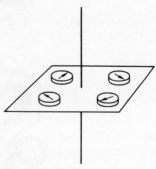

The compasses show that

- **A** there is a current flowing down the wire
- **B** there is a current flowing up the wire
- **C** there is no current in the wire
- **D** the wire is magnetised
- **E** the Earth's field is strong.

242 The strength of the magnetic field produced by a coil of wire can be increased by

- **1** inserting a copper core into the coil
- **2** increasing the current flowing through the coil
- **3** increasing the number of turns of wire on the coil.

243 Two iron rods are suspended inside a coil of wire as shown.

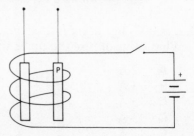

When the switch is closed,

- **1** looking down on the top of the coil, the current will flow anti-clockwise
- **2** the end of the rod marked P will be a north pole
- **3** the two rods will attract each other.

244 The diagram shows an electromagnet aligned east—west and connected to a battery. A compass is placed near by with its needle initially pointing to position Q as shown.

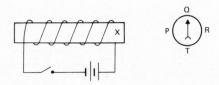

When the switch is closed,

   1 the end X becomes a north pole
   2 the needle is deflected to point to R
   3 if the battery is reversed the needle points to T.

245 Which of the following statements describing the action of an electric bell is false ?

   A When the switch is pressed, a current flows through the coil causing its core to become magnetised.
   B An iron armature is repelled causing a hammer to hit a bell.
   C The movement of the armature breaks the circuit and switches off the electromagnet.
   D A spring pulls the iron armature back, to complete the electric circuit again.
   E The sequence is repeated several times a second.

246 Fleming's rule for the direction of the force acting on a wire carrying a current in a magnetic field uses

   1 the left hand
   2 the first finger for the direction of the magnetic field
   3 the second finger for the direction of the current.

247 The diagram shows a wire carrying a current between the poles of a magnet.

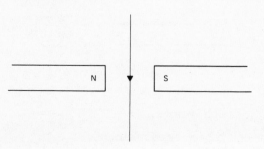

In which direction does the wire tend to move ?

  A Into the paper.
  B Out of the paper.
  C Towards the bottom of the page.
  D Towards the south pole of the magnet.
  E In some other direction.

248 Two long parallel wires PQ and XY are hanging side by side and connected to batteries as shown.

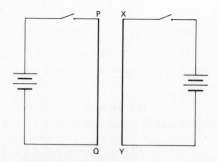

When both switches are closed,

  1 a current will flow in the direction PQ
  2 a current will flow in the direction XY
  3 the wires will tend to move towards each other.

Questions **249** and **250**.

The diagram shows a simple
d.c. electric motor.

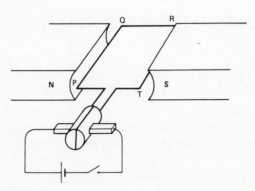

249 When the switch is closed,

1 a current will flow round the coil in the direction PQRT
2 the coil will rotate in a clockwise direction
3 the purpose of the commutator is to reverse the current after every complete cycle.

250 The direction of rotation will be reversed if

1 the battery is connected the other way round
2 the magnet's poles are interchanged
3 both of these are done at the same time.

Electromagnetic Induction

251 Fleming's rule for the direction of the current induced in a wire when it is moved across a magnetic field uses

1 the right hand
2 the first finger for the direction of the magnetic field
3 the thumb for the direction of the movement.

252 The diagram shows a wire between the poles of a magnet.

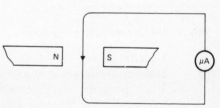

In which direction must the wire be moved in order to give a current as shown in the diagram ?

A Into the paper.
B Out of the paper.
C Towards the south pole.
D In the direction of the arrow.
E In some other direction.

Questions **253** to **255**.

The diagram shows a coil connected to a centre-zero galvanometer.

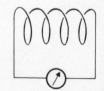

When the N-pole of the magnet is pushed into the coil, the galvanometer pointer is deflected to the right.

253 It can be deduced that

    1 if the magnet is then pulled out, the galvanometer pointer is deflected to the left

    2 if the S-pole is pushed in, the deflection is to the right

    3 if the S-pole is held stationary inside the coil, the deflection is to the right.

254 The deflection of the galvanometer can be increased by

    1 moving the magnet faster

    2 increasing the number of turns on the coil

    3 using a stronger magnet.

255 When the magnet is pushed into the coil, it affects the coil and causes a current to flow. What effect does the coil have on the magnet ?

    A The magnet is attracted.

    B The magnet is harder to move.

    C The magnet tends to move sideways.

    D The magnet tends to rotate.

    E None at all.

256 Which of the following will NOT increase the voltage produced by a dynamo ?

    A Using a stronger magnetic field.

    B Using thicker wire for the coil.

    C Using a soft-iron core inside the coil.

    D Increasing the number of turns on the coil.

    E Increasing the speed of rotation.

257 The chief energy conversion in the a.c. generator is

    A from mechanical energy to electrical energy

    B from electrical energy to mechanical energy

    C from mechanical energy to heat energy

    D from heat energy to electrical energy

    E from electrical energy to heat energy.

258 In a step-up transformer,

    1 the core should be laminated

    2 the primary coil and the secondary coil are linked by a magnetic field

    3 the output power is greater than the input power.

259 The diagram shows a simple transformer.

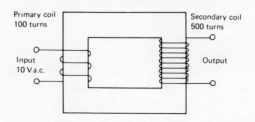

What voltage would you expect across the secondary coil ?

    A   2 V d.c.

    B   2 V a.c.

    C 10 V d.c.

    D 50 V d.c.

    E 50 V a.c.

260 Electrical energy is transmitted in the National Grid System at high voltages because

    A   some factories need very high voltages

    B   the generators at the power station rotate at high speed

    C   it is easier to generate high voltages

    D   energy losses in the cables are less at high voltages

    E   the resistance of the cables is less at high voltages.

Electron Physics

261 Cathode rays

  1 consist of electrons
  2 have a negative charge
  3 travel from the cathode to the anode.

262 Cathode rays

  1 produce X-rays when they hit a target
  2 produce light when they hit a fluorescent screen
  3 are electromagnetic waves.

263 The diagram shows a beam of electrons passing between a positively-charged plate and a negatively-charged plate.

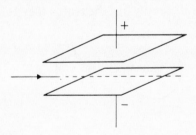

The electrons are

  A deflected towards the positive plate
  B deflected towards the negative plate
  C deflected out of the paper
  D deflected into the paper
  E not deflected.

264 The diagram shows a beam of electrons passing between the N-pole and S-pole of a magnet.

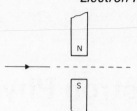

To work out the direction the electrons are deflected, the steps are :

1 electrons travelling from left to right behave like a conventional current flowing from right to left

2 the rule to use is Fleming's Left hand rule

3 the deflection is into the paper.

265 In a diode valve or a cathode ray oscilloscope, the electrons leave the surface of the cathode

1 only when it is hot

2 only when it is surrounded by a vacuum

3 only when the anode is positive.

266 Chris and Joanne are trying to use a C.R.O. to display the waveform of an a.c. supply but the traces they get are

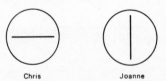

Which controls would you expect them to adjust to get the correct traces ?

	Chris	*Joanne*
A	X-time-base	Y-gain (amplification)
B	Y-gain (amplification)	X-time-base
C	X-shift	Y-shift
D	Y-shift	X-shift
E	Focus	Brilliance

Questions **267** to **270**.

The diagrams show some possible traces which could be obtained on the screen of a cathode ray oscilloscope.

A   B   C   D   E

With no input, a horizontal line was obtained at the centre of the screen. Which trace would you expect to obtain if the Y-plates are connected to

267 a battery ?

268 an a.c. supply ?

269 the output of a single diode rectifier ?

270 a supply which is a mixture of a.c. and d.c. ?

Atomic Structure

271 In an atom,

    1 the nucleus is positively charged
    2 most of the mass is concentrated in the nucleus
    3 the space between the nucleus and the electrons is filled with air.

272 The diagram shows a representation of an atom.

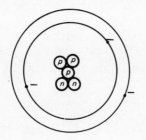

The correct way to write the formula for this atom of substance X is

    A $^{3}_{2}X$

    B $^{5}_{2}X$

    C $^{2}_{3}X$

    D $^{5}_{3}X$

    E $^{3}_{4}X$

Questions **273** to **278** are about a Radium atom which has an atomic number of 88 and a mass number of 226.

For each of the questions **273** to **277** choose your answer from the following list

A 88
B 138
C 226
D 314
E variable.

273 How many protons are there in a nucleus of this isotope of Radium ?

274 How many orbital electrons are there in a neutral atom of this isotope ?

275 How many nucleons (protons and neutrons) are there in a nucleus of this isotope ?

276 How many neutrons are there in a nucleus of this isotope ?

277 How many protons are there in the nuclei of other Radium isotopes ?

278 The correct way to write the formula for the Radium isotope described in the introduction to these questions is

A $^{138}_{88}Ra$ **B** $^{226}_{88}Ra$ **C** $^{226}_{138}Ra$ **D** $^{314}_{138}Ra$ **E** $^{88}_{226}Ra$.

279 Which of the following is also an isotope of Radium ?

A $^{226}_{87}X$ **B** $^{225}_{88}X$ **C** $^{227}_{89}X$ **D** $^{225}_{138}X$ **E** $^{87}_{226}X$.

280 Isotopes of an element have

    1 the same number of neutrons
    2 the same number of protons
    3 the same chemical properties.

Radioactivity

281 Which of the following can penetrate a piece of cardboard or a person's skin ?

    1 Alpha particles.
    2 Beta particles.
    3 Gamma rays.

282 A radioactive sample is tested using a thin-window Geiger tube. When a piece of paper is placed between the source and the tube, there is a large fall in the count rate. When the piece of paper is replaced by a thin sheet of lead, none of the radiation reaches the tube. This means that the source is emitting

    1 alpha particles
    2 beta particles
    3 gamma rays.

283 A stream of radiation is found to be deflected by a magnetic field. This means that the radiation could consist of

    1 alpha particles
    2 beta particles
    3 gamma rays.

284 Alpha particles

    1 are negatively charged
    2 are very penetrating
    3 consist of two protons and two neutrons.

285 Beta particles

    1 are strongly deflected by a magnetic field
    2 are electrons
    3 come from the nucleus of the atom.

286 Gamma rays

    1 travel at the speed of light
    2 can be stopped by a few millimetres of aluminium
    3 are positively charged.

287 A radioactive isotope X has a half-life of 1 day.
What fraction of X remains after 3 days ?

    A $\frac{1}{3}$

    B $\frac{1}{4}$

    C $\frac{1}{6}$

    D $\frac{1}{8}$

    E   none.

Questions **288** and **289**.

The graph shows the results of an experiment in which the
activity of a radioactive source was measured over a period of
6 hours.

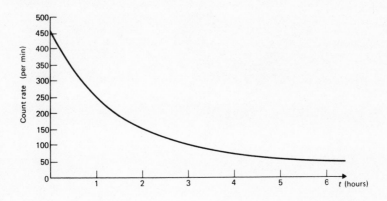

288 From the graph, the background count rate is approximately

    A   zero
    B   50 per minute
    C   100 per minute
    D   250 per minute
    E   450 per minute.

289 After correcting the count rate for the background radiation, it can be deduced that the half-life of the substance is

    A   1 hour

    B $1\frac{1}{4}$ hours

    C   3 hours

    D   6 hours

    E   225 hours.

290 When a $^{226}_{88}$Ra nucleus decays radioactively by the emission of an alpha particle, the nucleus remaining is

    A $^{226}_{89}$Ac

    B $^{222}_{86}$Rn

    C $^{224}_{86}$Rn

    D $^{222}_{84}$Po

    E $^{224}_{84}$Po.

Graphs

Questions **291** to **300**.

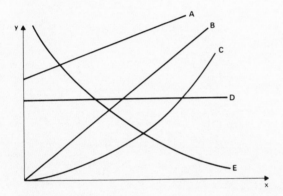

From the five graphs shown above, select which most nearly shows the following relationships (in each case the first quantity is plotted on the Y-axis).

291 Temperature of a beaker of hot water against time as it cools.

292 Velocity against time for an object travelling with zero acceleration.

293 Velocity against time for an object travelling with uniform acceleration from rest.

294 Extension against load for an elastic spring.

295 Volume against temperature for a fixed mass of mercury.

296 Current through a wire at constant temperature against voltage across it.

297 Volume of a fixed mass of gas at constant pressure against temperature in °C.

298 Distance travelled by a freely-falling body against time.

299 Pressure against volume for a fixed mass of gas at constant temperature.

300 Heat produced in a wire against current flowing.